KU-444-055

Alan Turing's
MATHS GAMES
FOR KIDS

ARCTURUS

Use this code throughout the book to solve puzzles!

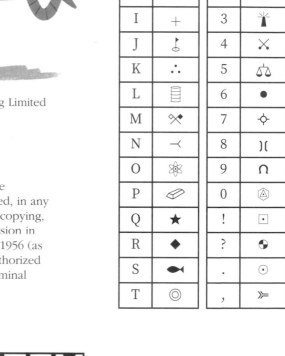

A	❄	U	⬡
B	◇	V	□
C	▲	W	♕
D	🌡	X	🚦
E	☆	Y	○
F	◪	Z	◈
G	✪	1	▲
H	⚠	2	■
I	+	3	☀
J	♪	4	✕
K	∴	5	⚖
L	▤	6	●
M	⚒	7	◇
N	⊣	8	)(
O	⚛	9	∩
P	▱	0	⬡
Q	★	!	⊡
R	◆	?	◓
S	🐟	.	⊙
T	◎	,	⋙

ARCTURUS

This edition published in 2021 by Arcturus Publishing Limited
26/27 Bickels Yard, 151–153 Bermondsey Street,
London SE1 3HA

Copyright © Arcturus Holdings Limited
The Turing Trust logo © The Turing Trust

All rights reserved. No part of this publication may be reproduced, stored in a retrieval system, or transmitted, in any form or by any means, electronic, mechanical, photocopying, recording, or otherwise, without prior written permission in accordance with the provisions of the Copyright Act 1956 (as amended). Any person or persons who do any unauthorized act in relation to this publication may be liable to criminal prosecution and civil claims for damages.

Author: William Potter
Illustrator: Gareth Conway
Designer: Well Nice Studio
Design Manager: Jessica Holliland
Managing Editor: Joe Harris

ISBN: 978-1-83940-719-2
CH008262NT
Supplier 29, Date 1220, Print run 10673

Printed in China

What is STEM?

STEM is a world-wide initiative that aims to cultivate an interest in Science, Technology, Engineering, and Mathematics, in an effort to promote these disciplines to as wide a variety of students as possible.

Hello, I'm Alan. Welcome to my magical, mathematical puzzle book!

ALL ABOUT ALAN

Alan Turing was born in London in 1912. He was a mathematical genius whose ideas helped develop modern computing.

During World War II, Alan played an important role at Bletchley Park in the UK. He helped design a machine called the "Bombe." The machine was used to decode messages from the German military.

Alan Turing's code-breaking skills helped the Allies shorten the war and saved many lives.

THE TURING TRUST

When you buy this book, you are supporting The Turing Trust. This is a charity, set up by Alan's family, in his memory.

The Turing Trust works with communities in Africa to give people access to computers.

Eggs-tra eggs

These eggs have been collected into groups that belong in the same times table—but one egg is wrong for each group. Which one?

Group A

25 10 60 5 35 15 45 53 40

Group B

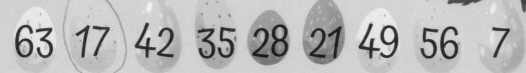

63 17 42 35 28 21 49 56 7

Group C

111 77 99 55 66 11 88 33 44

Group D

99 27 18 72 63 54 35 81 45

Sheep sets

Help round up the sheep into pairs. All the paired numbers should add up to 54. Which sheep number goes with which?

47 11 9 43 12 46
5 15 37 17 28 32
22 19 29
33
23 16 25 45
31 35
13
39 41 26
49 42
7 8 21
38

Alan Turing's Challenge

How many of the sheep have prime numbers?

Freshly picked

Check out these bargain prices for fruit and vegetables.
How much will each plate cost?

Which is the most expensive?

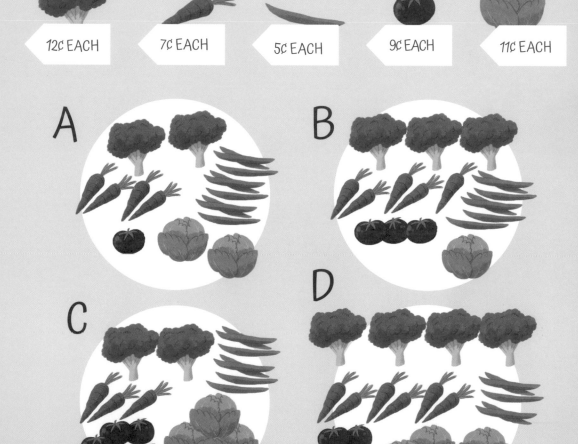

12¢ EACH   7¢ EACH   5¢ EACH   9¢ EACH   11¢ EACH

A

B

C

D

Wheel away

Three bike and scooter riders raced each other around a five-mile-long track. Which order did they finish in?

Juliet set off first and scooted at 10 m.p.h. for 10 minutes, then 8 m.p.h. for 10 minutes, then 6 m.p.h. for the rest of the race.

Dylan set off 5 minutes after Juliet. He scooted at 12 m.p.h. for 15 minutes, then 6 m.p.h. for the rest of the race.

Billie set off 10 minutes after Juliet and cycled at 15 m.p.h. for 12 minutes, then 8 m.p.h. for the rest of the race.

Alan Turing's Challenge

Use the code on page 2 to discover a fun fact!

◎△+◆◎○　✐☆◆▲☆⌐◎　❋◪　❋▤▤　◎◆+✐✐　+⌐　◎△☆

⌐☆◎△☆◆▤❋⌐◊✉　❋◆☆　✗❋◊☆　◇○　◇+▲◎▲▤☆☉

Spell solutions

Whitebeard the wizard has conjured a calculation spell. What result will he get for each of the circled numbers? Answer each step before moving on to the next calculation.

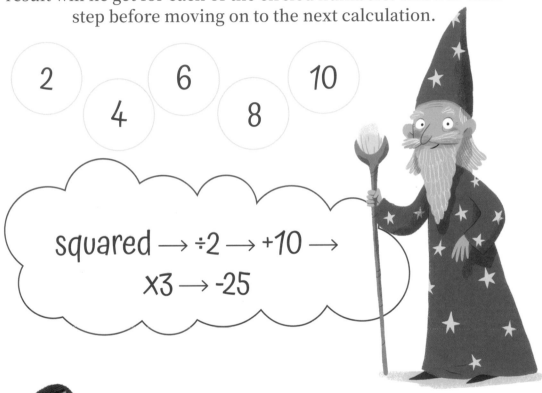

2   6   10
  4   8

squared → ÷2 → +10 →
x3 → -25

Alan Turing's Challenge

The spell has gone wrong! The wizard has put in the number 20 but the answer is 185. Which step was missed?

Airlines

The numbers along the routes on this sky map equal the tons of fuel used by a jet. Which route from A to B uses the least fuel?

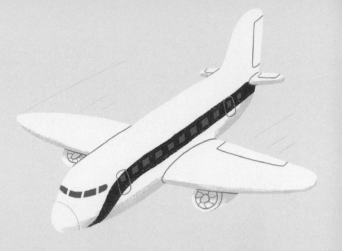

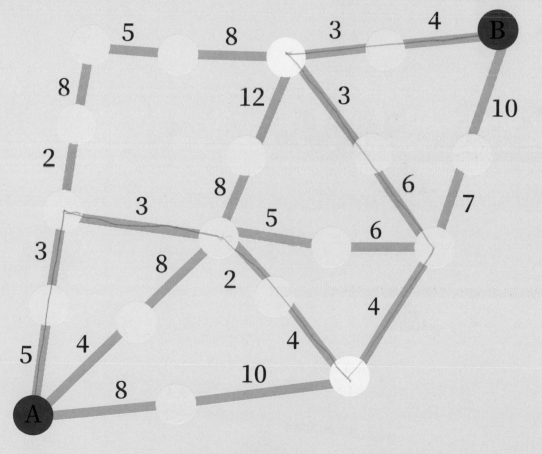

Pet parade

Compare the weights of the pets on the balances to work out the order of the pets from lightest to heaviest.

Unicorn party

All the magic realm's unicorns have gathered for a festival. Count how many there are, then work out the percentage of the different groups.

What percentage of the unicorns ...

... are blue?

... are pink?

... are neither pink nor blue?

... have purple manes?

... have yellow manes?

Alan Turing's Challenge

Five more unicorns join the group, all with green manes.
What percentage of the unicorns have green manes?

Pyramid pieces

On this pyramid the number on each block is the
sum of the numbers on the two blocks below it.
Fill in the missing numbers.

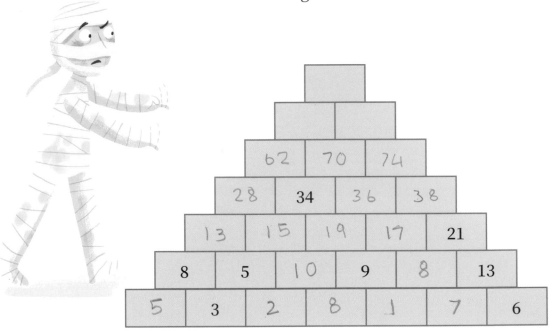

Alan Turing's Challenge

Use the code on page 2 to discover a fun fact!

●◄☆◆□❊◄◎●◄ ❊◪ ❊ ⎍☆❄⎍ ☆⊛○⬭◎+❊◄ ⬭△❊◆❊◪△

⋔⩙☆◆☆ ❊◪◎☆◄ ●◄☆❄⊟☆⎍ +◄ △+●◄ ⬭○◆❊✕+⎍ ⋔⩙+◎△

△+✕◆➢ ⎍☆❊⎍ ❊◆ ❊⊟+□☆·

Monster mission

In this monster-sized suduko puzzle, write the numbers from 1 to 9 into the empty squares, so that each row, each column, and each 3x3 box of nine squares contains all the numbers from 1 to 9.

1		3		8				2
	7			5				
5	8	4			1			7
2		5	8					
7			6		4			1
					5	2		6
3			7			1	8	4
				3			7	
9				4		6		3

Bargain beater

The sale is on! Which offer gets you the cheapest price for one pair of cool trainers?

$75 each. 3 for the price of 2

¼ off $60

Was $84. Now half price!

10% off $50

20% off $70

⅓ off $60

30% off $80

Alan Turing's Challenge

The cheapest price isn't always the best value.
Can you work out which offer gives you the biggest saving
from the original price of the trainers?

Sky high

Which hot-air balloon has won the race? Cross out all the prime numbers and numbers that are multiples of 3 to find out.

Star chart

Starting on the white arrow, guide the astronaut across the star map. The numbers show how many squares you need to move, followed by an arrow giving the direction. Read the directions from left to right, starting with the top row. Where do you end up?

2 ↑	2 →	2 ↑	1 ←	2 ↑	3 →	6 ↓	5 →	4 ↑	2 ←
2 ↑	2 →	2 ↑	1 ←	1 ↑	3 ←	4 ↓	3 →	3 ↓	1 ←

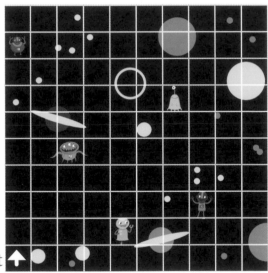

Start

Alan Turing's Challenge

Use the code on page 2 to discover the answer to the following question:
Who has spent the most time in space?

▲❀➤⤢❄⊰❀●◎ ⊗☆⊰⤢❀◖○ ▱❀◖❀▤∴❀ △❀➤ ➤◖▱☆⊰◎

)(✧)(◖❀○➤ +⊰ ➤◖▱❀▲☆ ❀□☆◆ ◤+□☆ ⤢+➤➤◖+❀⊰➤●◎

Gone fishing

What has the gnome caught with his fishing line? Complete the dot-to-dot puzzle following multiples of four only to reveal his catch.

18
22
20
78 16
8
24 30
6 4 12
100 2
26
39 38 34 35
95 5 39
86 37
85 29 47
82 41 46
83 79 10
78 49
28 45
32
82 96 92
77 88 94 43
75 80
72 84 50 36
64 68 76
74 71 48 40 42
73 44
70 55
60
69 51 57
63 56 52 55
58 53 57
61 59 54
62

Bake contest

Who won the baking competition?

Add up all the prize points for each baker to find the cook with the highest overall score.

🏆 1 — 50	🏆 2 — 30	🏆 3 — 15
🎖 1 — 40	🎖 2 — 20	🎖 3 — 10
🎗 1 — 30	🎗 2 — 25	🎗 3 — 15

Brian

Jess

Martin

Cedric

Alan Turing's Challenge

One baker won 5 cups and achieved a total of 110 points. What cups did they win?

18

Bug bonanza

Look at the totals for each row and column in the bug count.
Then work out how many of each bug was counted.
The number of bees is already given.

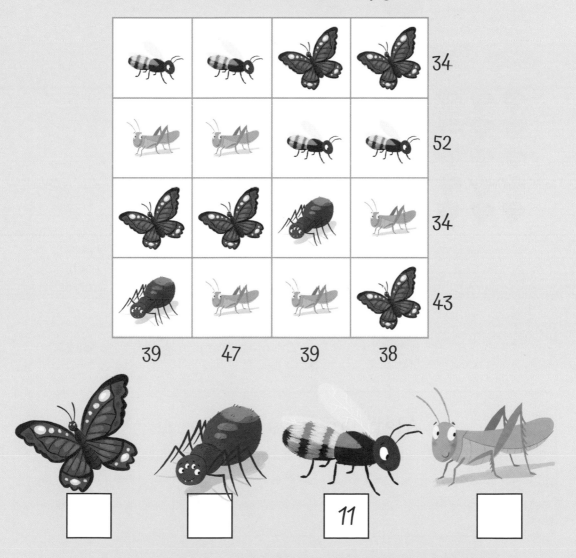

Sparkly sums

Read the clues to work out how much this collection
of shiny jewels is worth.

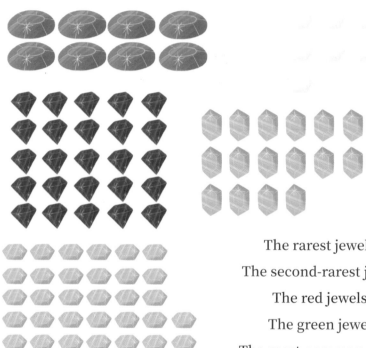

The rarest jewels = $12 each.

The second-rarest jewels = $9 each.

The red jewels = $13 for 5.

The green jewels = $9 for 3.

The most-common jewels = $6 for 2.

Alan Turing's Challenge

Use the code on page 2 to discover a fun fact!

⚗+❄✂❄⤙⚗ +🐟 ✂❄⚗⚗☆ ◪◆❄✂ ◎△☆ ☆🛢☆✂☆⤙◎

▲❄◆◇❄⤙≻ 🛢+∴☆ ◎△☆ ★◆❄🔔⬭△+◎☆ +⤙ ⬭☆⤙▲+🛢🐟⊙

Going dotty

In the game of dominoes, the pieces form a chain with matching numbers of dots touching each other.

Copy the dots from the dominoes along the bottom of the page to complete the chain. Four dominoes are already in place.

Vanishing act

Wizarding Will has made the mathematical symbols disappear in these calculations. Can you work out what they were to make the answers correct?

12 ? 5 ? 4 = 64

8 ? 9 ? 17 = 55

5 ? 10 ? 2 = 25

40 ? 8 ? 11 = 55

9 ? 6 ? 2 = 27

7 ? 5 ? 13 = 48

Alan Turing's Challenge

Use the code on page 2 to discover a fun fact!

◎△☆　☆❄◆▤+☆🐟◎　∴⊰❋ᴡ⊰　●🐟☆　❋◪　◎△☆

✕●▤◎+◻▤+▲❋◎+❋⊰　🐟○✕◇❋▤　+⊰　✕❄◎△☆✕❄◎+▲●

ᴡ❄●◀　+⊰　♠●♠)(⊙

Robot revolution

Each of these robots' dials has been given a series of turns.
Draw an arrow on each blank dial to show its final position.

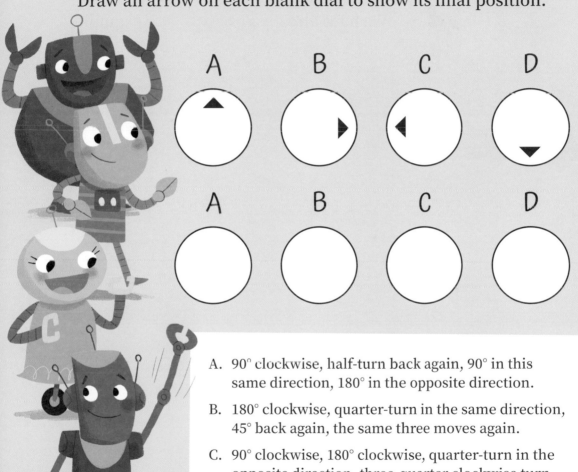

A. 90° clockwise, half-turn back again, 90° in this same direction, 180° in the opposite direction.

B. 180° clockwise, quarter-turn in the same direction, 45° back again, the same three moves again.

C. 90° clockwise, 180° clockwise, quarter-turn in the opposite direction, three-quarter clockwise turn.

D. Three-quarter clockwise turn, 90° clockwise, 45° in the opposite direction, 135° clockwise.

Symmetry sketch

Help the builder with her planning by marking
all the lines of symmetry on each shape.
We have already given you one example.

Cake compare

All the scales below are evenly balanced. Given the weight of one baked treat, can you work out the weight of all the others?

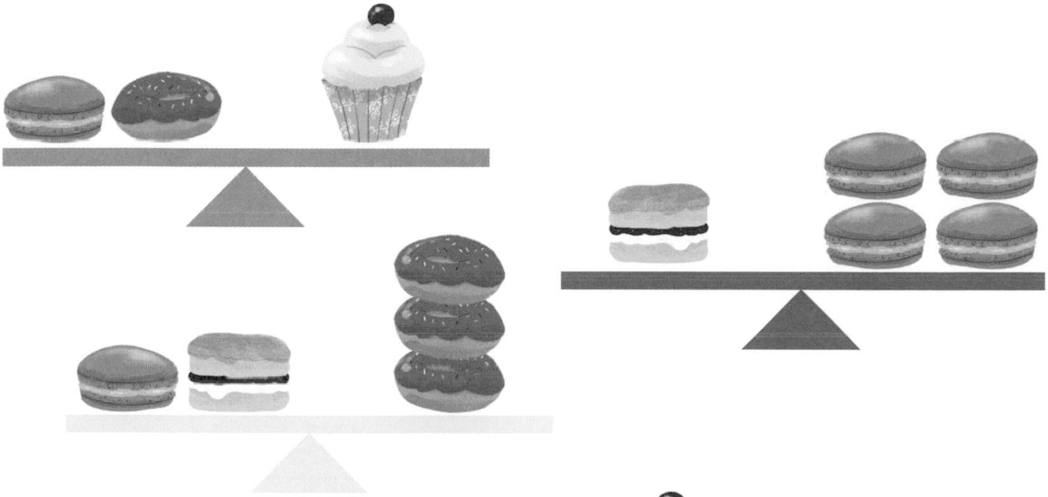

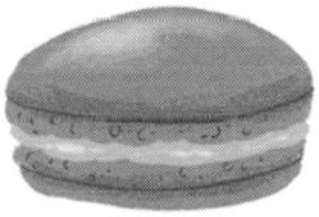	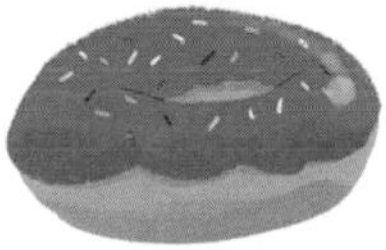	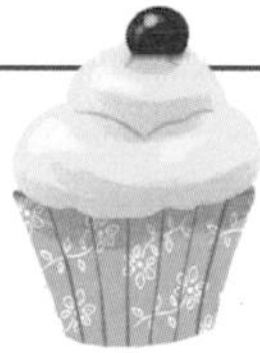	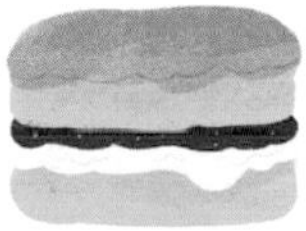
	5		

Alan Turing's Challenge

Use the code on page 2 to discover the answer to the following question: What's the difference between a cake and a cookie?

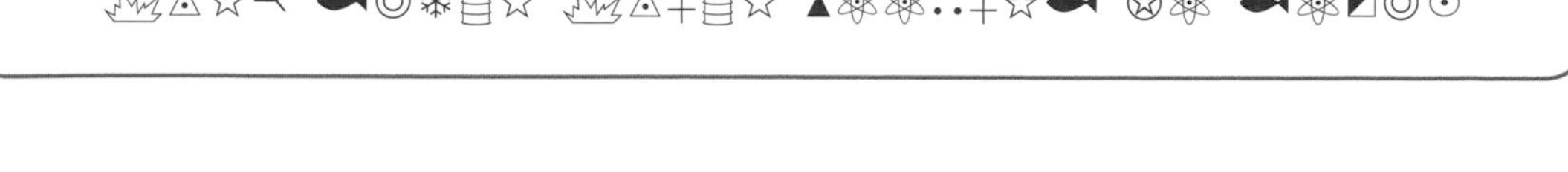

Number snakes

Fill in the missing numbers 1 to 5 in the circles below so that the numbers appear just once in every row, column and snaking set of connected circles.

Calculation chains

For each chain, take the first number and pass it through all of the calculations to find out the number in the last link. Answer each step before moving on to the next calculation.

A | 4 | x 6 | ÷ 2 | + 8 | x 5 | - 20 | ?

B | 12 | x 5 | - 10 | ÷ 5 | + 6 | x 4 | ?

C | 7 | + 8 | x 4 | - 6 | ÷ 6 | x 11 | ?

D | 25 | - 9 | ÷ 4 | x 7 | + 12 | ÷ 5 | ?

Alan Turing's Challenge

Have a look at your answers. Why is C the odd one out?

27

Raising sums

Place a number from 1 to 9 into each empty square, so that the numbers in each row add up to the number in the triangle on the left, and the numbers in each column add up to the number in the triangle above it.

	12	26		25	10
5	4		15 / 19		9
25		3	9		
7 / 15		7		5	8
23			7		
11	2		13		5

Clown clocks

All the clown clocks go at different speeds. If all the clocks are set to 2 o'clock, draw the hands on the clocks to show what time they will read after 3 hours and 5 hours.

Clock A gains 5 minutes every hour.

Clock B loses 15 minutes every hour.

Clock C gains 30 minutes every hour.

Clock D loses 40 minutes every hour.

A after 3 hours

A after 5 hours

B after 3 hours

B after 5 hours

C after 3 hours

C after 5 hours

D after 3 hours

D after 5 hours

Alan Turing's Challenge

Use the code on page 2 to discover the answer to the following question:
Who decided there should be 60 minutes in an hour?

Code cracker

Be a super-spy and unlock the
number code from the clues.

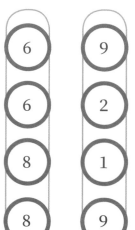

6	9	4	One number is correct and in the right position.
6	2	7	One number is correct but in the wrong position.
8	1	9	No numbers are correct.
8	9	3	One number is correct but in the wrong position.
4	3	6	Two numbers are correct but in the wrong position.

Alan Turing's Challenge

Look at the answer to the code.

A. Can your answer be divided exactly by 9?

B. Can your answer be divided exactly by 11?

C. Can your answer be divided exactly by 15?

Temple task

Eliza the explorer is looking for a lost temple. Can you find it? Each time she visits a location on the map, she can see one square away in all directions.

Mark all of Eliza's co-ordinates on the map, plus the squares next to them—up, down, across, and diagonally. The temple is found in the only square she has not visited or been next to. Where is it?

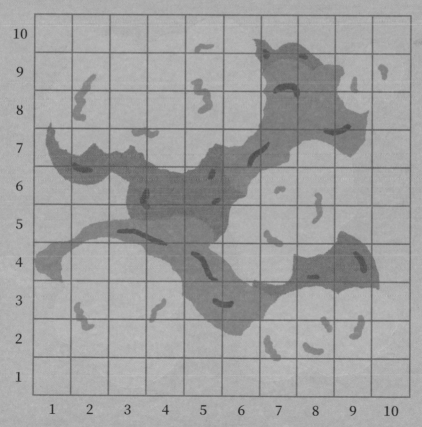

These co-ordinates are horizontal first, then vertical: (1, 3) (1, 9) (2,1) (2,6) (4,4) (4,9) (5,2) (5,7) (6,10) (7,1) (7,5) (8,7) (9,2) (9,10) (10,5) (10,8)

Brick by brick

Help Brad the brickie complete
these three walls.

First, add together the numbered bricks in each of
the three walls below. Then, choose three bricks from
the bottom of the page that add up to the same totals
and write them into the blank bricks.

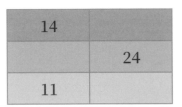

14	
	24
11	

17	
	31
9	

33	
	15
22	

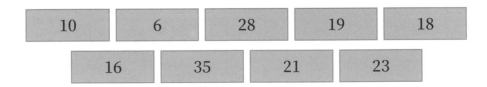

10	6	28	19	18

16	35	21	23

Alan Turing's Challenge

Use the code on page 2 to discover a fun fact!

◎△☆ +⌐◊☆⌐◎✳◎+✳⌐ ✳⌐ ✳ ◇◆+▲∴ +◂ ▲✳🗐☆◊ ✳

◪◆✳⊗⊡⊡

Fishy business

Myrtle Turtle is thinking of one number that a fish has blown in a bubble.

Read the clues and cross out the numbers to work out what it is.

45 48 11 10 4 50 19 25 38 3 20 43 32 49 31 29 24 14 2 9 16 23 8 15 26 18 46 30 7 28 41 6 27 33 21 36 34 40 13 17 47 5 42 39 44 22 35 12 37

It is not a prime number.

It is not exactly divisible by three.

It is not an even number.

It is not in the 5 times table.

BETTY'S BURGER MENU

Beefburger or veggie burger
Choice of toppings:

Cheese	Tomato	Mustard
Onion	Gherkin	Ketchup

All in order

A huge order has come in at Betty's Burgers.
How many of each ingredient does Betty need?

One onion is enough for six burgers, one tomato is enough for three burgers, and one gherkin is enough for two burgers.

Eighteen people want a burger.

Four of them are vegetarian.

All but three want cheese.

Six do not like onions.

Two thirds of the group want tomatoes

Half of the meat-eaters and one vegetarian don't like gherkins.

Ten do not want mustard or ketchup.

Of the rest, half want mustard, half ketchup.

Betty needs:

	Beefburgers
	Veggie burgers
	Slices of cheese
	Onions
	Tomatoes
	Gherkins
	Servings of mustard
	Servings of ketchup

Working backward

Aliens from the planet Htrae do their mathematics backward. What is the first number in each of these calculations?

$? \times 6 + 3 = 39$

$? \times 6 \times 25 = 300$

$? - 4 - 18 = 4$

$? + 29 + 3 = 82$

$? \times 4 \times 2 = 72$

$? \div 10 \div 10 = 1$

Alan Turing's Challenge

Now how about this one?

$? \div 5 \div 3 \div 10 = 3$

1, 2, 3, 4!

Hiding in this grid is a group of four numbers that add up to exactly 24. The four numbers are arranged in a square, with two rows and two columns. Can you find the group?

5	7	6	3	2	8	9	6
2	8	1	8	4	7	1	7
6	5	8	2	9	3	8	5
1	9	3	7	5	6	2	4
3	5	8	4	9	5	8	7
8	4	9	6	7	4	5	2
3	7	5	4	5	9	8	6
9	3	8	3	8	5	1	7

Alan Turing's Challenge

Use the code on page 2 to discover the answer to the following question:
What instrument was famously designed by George Beauchamp?

◎△+🐟 ❋✖☆◆+▲❋⊰ +⊰□☆⊰◎❋◆ ❋◪ ✖●🐟⊰+▲❋🗄

+⊰🐟◎◆⬡✖☆⊰◎● 🗄❋●⊰▲△☆ↅ ◎△☆ ◪+◆🐟◎

☆🗄☆▲◎◆+▲ ★●+◎❋◆ +⊰ ⚡∩ℾ⅄⬥⊙

36

Snowfall

One winter's day, Jake and Jenny decide to make a record of how much snow has fallen.

In the first hour, from 8–9am, they record two inches of snow in their measuring beaker.

The beaker fills up twice as fast for the next four hours.

Then it fills up by 3 inches per hour until 3pm.

The next four hours, snow falls at 2.5 inches per hour.

In the remaining time before they stop recording, at 9pm, the beaker gains another 5 inches of snow.

How many inches of snow fell altogether?

(What a snowy day!)

Numbers go round

Fill the empty squares with the numbers 1 to 9.

Each number can only be used once in the squares. The number in each circle is the result of multiplying together the four numbers in the squares around it.

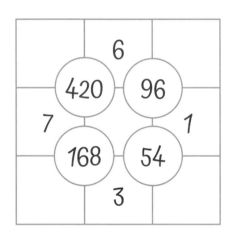

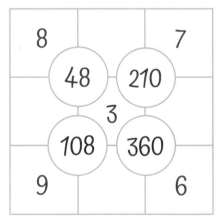

Alan Turing's Challenge

Use the code on page 2 to discover a fun fact!

▲✳◎⬢ ▲✳⤙⤙⚛◎ ◎✳⬢◎☆ ⬢↳↲☆☆◎⤙☆⬢⬢⬢⊙

Cycle tracks

Ben cycled between points on a map to make a picture. Join the co-ordinates in order to see what he drew.

These co-ordinates are horizontal first, then vertical: (1,2) (1,4) (3,5) (2,5) (1,6) (1,8) (2,10) (2,8) (3,9) (3,7) (2,7) (2,6) (3,6) (4,7) (6,7) (7,6) (8,6) (9,7) (8,8) (9,10) (9,8) (10,10) (10,7) (8,5) (7,5) (9,4) (10,3) (8,4) (7,4) (8,3) (8,1) (7,3) (6,4) (4,4) (3,3) (3,1) (2,3) (3,4) (2,4) (1,2)

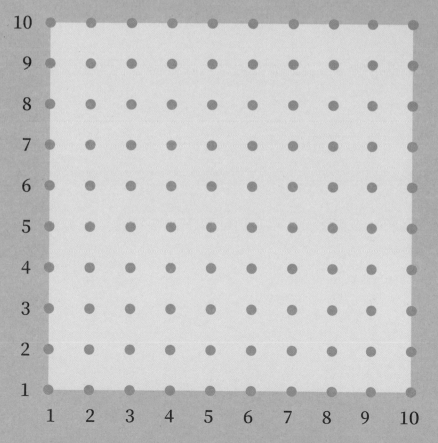

Square spells

Use your math-magical powers to draw lines linking numbers to their squares. We have added an example to get you started.

144

4

8

64

100

81

2

36

10,000

49

9

6

5

10

169

121

100

3

7

11

9

16

12

4

13

Safari sequences

What number comes next in each of these sequences?

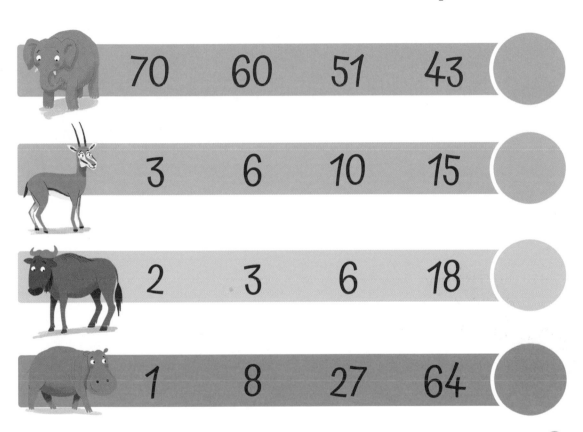

70   60   51   43

3   6   10   15

2   3   6   18

1   8   27   64

Alan Turing's Challenge

Use the code on page 2 to discover the answer to the following question:
How high can elephants jump?

☆🗄☆✏△❋⤙◎🐟 ▲❋⤙⤙⚛◎ 🔑●✖✏☉

Beach beat

Can you draw a continuous line across the shells from start to finish? You may move up, down, and through, but not diagonally. You may only tread on shells with numbers that are multiples of 3.

Start

33	2	19	4	56	11	4	101
9	5	10	47	25	15	93	96
12	15	21	3	7	12	28	18
26	44	19	6	89	27	4	12
20	30	18	27	14	21	34	303
205	21	34	1	22	99	40	333
8	36	9	300	66	3	20	6
35	26	17	5	100	80	9	600

Finish

Cross clues

Solve the equations, then fill in the answers, one digit per square in the crossword-style grid.

ACROSS

1. 5 x 25
2. 12 x 7
4. 6 x 8
6. 11 x 100
7. 10,000 - 895
11. 600 - 44
12. 20^2

DOWN

1. 12^2
2. 20 x 20 x 20
3. 888 + 222
5. 1,000 - 111
8. 60 + 70
9. 50 x 11
10. 8^2

Alan Turing's Challenge

Use the code on page 2 to discover a fun fact!

Digging in

What area in square yards is each gardener's veg plot?

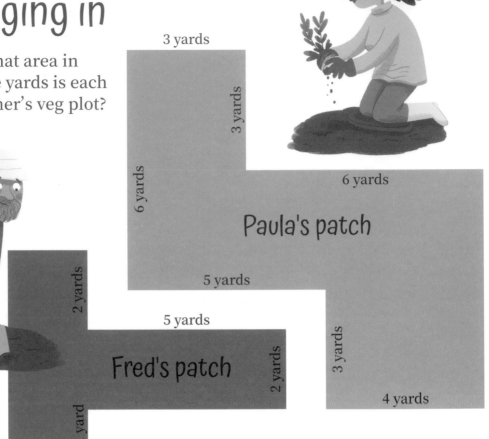

3 yards

3 yards

6 yards

6 yards

Paula's patch

5 yards

2 yards

5 yards

Fred's patch

2 yards

3 yards

1 yard

4 yards

2 yards

Alan Turing's Challenge

Use the code on page 2 to discover the answer to the following question:
Where do potatoes come from?

44

Suspect sums

This police officer is on the trail of six sneaky numbers. Each group of numbers below should add up to the total given. But two numbers need to be removed from each group for that to happen. Can you catch them?

100 Group A
18   7
9   22   23
6   3
26   16

109 Group B
17   19
4   20   16
22   24
14   8

125 Group C
6   16
30   10
15
8   22
14   29

Ski slopes

Can you work out the missing angles on the ski slopes?

Hint: Angles inside a triangle add up to 180°. Angles that form a semi-circle add up to 180°.

35°

e

a

b   c

d

50°   90°   90°   55°   90°   70°

To the rescue

The Riot City Rescue Rangers have had a busy week capturing super-criminals. Look at the graph and answer the questions on their amazing feats.

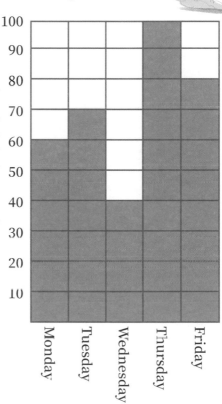

1. How many criminals did the Rescue Rangers capture over the whole week?

2. Which day did they capture 50% fewer criminals than Friday?

3. Did they capture more criminals from Monday to Wednesday or from Thursday to Friday—or was it the same?

Alan Turing's Challenge

How many more criminals were caught on the busiest day compared to the least busy?

It's a draw!

Draw paths from one square to another, horizontally or vertically (never diagonally), to join each matching pair of numbers.

1							
2	3		4	5		6	
			3				4
			1				
						5	
					7	8	
		9	2				
	9	7			8	6	

No line may enter a square containing a number, or a part of another path. All the squares must be used.

At all costs

These friends are visiting a foreign country that uses a different currency. What is the smallest combination of coins each of them can use to buy lunch without getting change?

Gary

50¢ 50¢ 50¢ 20¢ 20¢ 20¢ 20¢ 20¢ 20¢ 5¢ 5¢ 10¢ 10¢

Melanie

20¢ 20¢ 20¢ 20¢ 20¢ 50¢ 50¢ 5¢ 5¢ 5¢ 10¢ 10¢ 10¢ 10¢ 10¢

They both buy a hot dog costing 90¢, a burger costing 75¢, and an ice cream costing 60¢.

Alan Turing's Challenge

After paying for his food, Gary wants to buy his friend a hot dog. Does he have enough money?

Number crunchin' dinosaur

Fit the numbers in the grid, one dino digit per square.

21 27 42

304 356 458 494 724

1054 1872 7365 7939 9127 9520

51223 52710 60180 62248

166715 174236 512147 857716

Road race

Four cars set off on a 200-mile journey.
How long do they each take, and which arrives first?

A

Car A drives at
50 m.p.h. for half
the journey, stops
for 15 minutes,
then continues at
40 m.p.h. for the
rest of the journey.

B

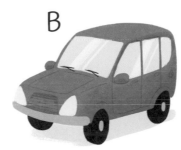

Car B drives at
40 m.p.h. for one
hour, 50 m.p.h.
for half an hour,
stops for
10 minutes, then
continues at
60 m.p.h. until
the finish.

C

Car C drives at
30 m.p.h. for
90 minutes, 50
m.p.h. for an hour,
stops for 30 minutes,
then continues at
70 m.p.h. for the rest
of the journcy.

D

Alan Turing's Challenge

Car D drives at 45 m.p.h. for one hour, stops for 10
minutes, continues at 60 m.p.h. for 45 minutes, stops for
another 10 minutes, then continues at 55 m.p.h. to the
finish. Does it beat the previous winner?

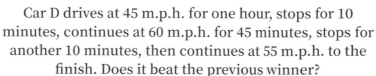

Giant germs

The doctors are fighting oversized germs. Last week there were 60 red rash germs, 75 blue goo germs, and 80 green meanies.

Count the remaining germs below to work out what percentage of each type of germ the doctors have got rid of.

Alan Turing's Challenge

Use the code on page 2 to discover a fun fact!

Cube collection

How many cubes are in this pile? Above the lowest tier, any visible block is supported by one other block directly below it, so no block is floating in mid-air.

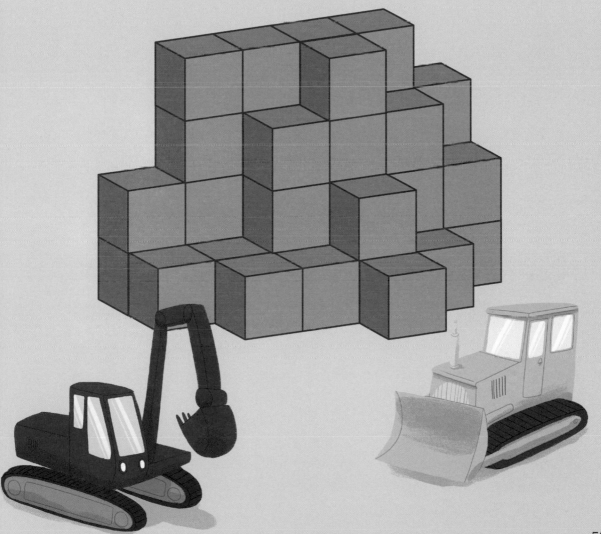

On the rebound

Which basketball bounces the highest?
Circle the one that matches all of these descriptions.

1. An even number

2. A square of another number on a basketball

3. A number with two digits

4. A date in a month

No time to waste

There's an emergency, and the rescue vehicles must hurry to the scene. The numbers show the distances along each road. Which is the quickest route?

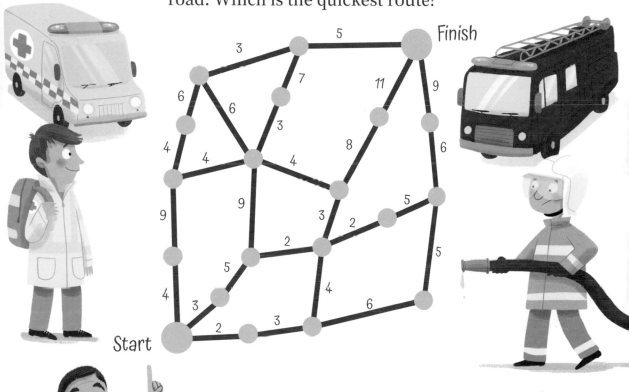

Finish

Start

Alan Turing's Challenge

Can you find a route that uses only odd numbers?
What distance is that?

Lucky fours

Find a way through the hexagons only stepping on numbers in the 4 times table to reach the lucky four-leaf clover. You cannot step on a number more than once.

Start

Finish

Nuts for all!

Share out these nuts so the 6 squirrels get the same number of each. How many does each get? (How many would 4 squirrels get? How many would 3 squirrels get?)

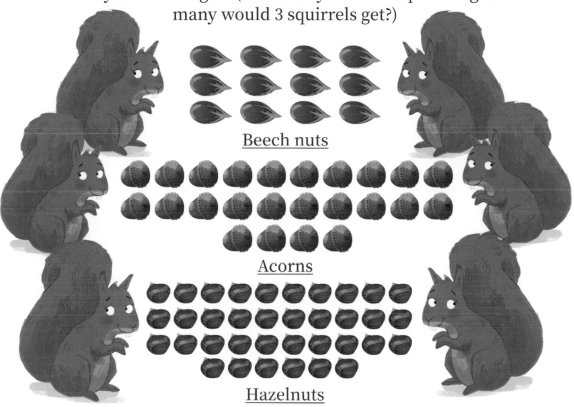

Beech nuts

Acorns

Hazelnuts

Alan Turing's Challenge

Use the code on page 2 to discover a fun fact!

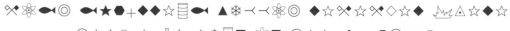

Going far

How far did each of these sporty kids travel today?

Cindy skateboarded at 6 m.p.h. for 20 minutes, walked at 4 m.p.h. for 30 minutes, skateboarded at 9 m.p.h. for half an hour, then repeated the same journey to get home.

Brian is training for a race. He ran for 45 minutes at 8 m.p.h. After a rest, he ran at 6 m.p.h. for 30 minutes, then half that speed for another half hour. Then he did a quick 10-minute sprint at 12 m.p.h.

Josie cycled around the park at a gentle 6 m.p.h. for 45 minutes. After pushing her bike at 3 m.p.h. for 20 minutes, she cycled again, at 8 m.p.h. for 15 minutes and 6 m.p.h. for 30 minutes.

Slice and dice

Lady Chopalot has cut these shapes into pieces. What fraction of the original shape has she cut away (the shaded part)?

A  Fraction =

B Fraction =

C Fraction =

D Fraction =

E Fraction =

Alan Turing's Challenge

Now give the cut out part of each shape as a percentage.

Stolen symbols

Oh no! Kat Burglar has stolen the symbols from these calculations. Can you work out which symbol (+ − × or ÷) belongs in each to make the answer correct?

$$4 \; ? \; 7 \; ? \; 11 = 39$$

$$20 \; ? \; 5 \; ? \; 10 = 90$$

$$54 \; ? \; 6 \; ? \; 5 = 45$$

$$36 \; ? \; 4 \; ? \; 6 = 15$$

$$32 \; ? \; 4 \; ? \; 26 = 34$$

Alan Turing's Challenge

Now try this one! 11 ? 6 ? 3 = 22

Ghost hunt

Help the ghost hunters find a path through the haunted house. Add up the numbers along the way to count how many ghosts they captured. What's the total?

Start ●

Finish ●

Fit for a king

Shade in all the prime numbers to reveal the picture.

67	12	7	28	47	66	4	37	70	19	50	83
41	13	71	97	3	44	12	29	7	53	5	73
23	79	31	2	62	20	58	61	17	89	11	31
45	83	41	61	10	1	42	34	7	41	79	30
8	11	21	59	51	47	23	74	71	40	29	18
57	5	6	43	33	31	5	76	2	60	43	9
65	5	89	17	19	13	83	17	53	3	61	75
35	73	39	97	31	64	72	19	29	24	67	25
56	59	15	67	3	22	32	13	11	52	23	68
27	29	71	43	37	48	69	43	97	73	37	54
3	11	19	2	79	7	53	89	23	59	2	17
77	46	85	26	55	47	13	36	49	63	16	38

Roman remains

Help the historian find out about the past by answering these calculations using only Roman numerals.

1. IX – II =

2. IV + VII =

3. VIII – V =

4. XXII + IX =

5. XXX – IV =

Alan Turing's Challenge

Now try this one! XV + XXII =

On the level

Look at the shapes on the top two balances.

What one shape can you add to the left side of the bottom balance to make both sides even?

Alan Turing's Challenge

Use the code on page 2 to discover the answer to the following question:
What was the highest tightrope walk?

+⌐ ■◉▲▲ ◕⌐◎●⌐◎✕❋⌐ ◪◆☆◊◊○ ⌐❋▲▲∴ ◕⌐☆◎ ❋ ⌐☆ᨓ

ᨓ❋◆▤◊ ◆☆▲❋◆◊ ◇○ ◎+⊕△◎◆❋▭◇☆ ᨓ❋▤∴+⌐⊕

◇☆◎ᨓ☆☆⌐ ◎ᨓ❋ ◕⌐ᨓ+◕◕ ▭☆❋∴◕⊙

Three is a crowd

Which two of the juggler's numbers added together will make each total? You can only use each number once.

TOTAL 26

TOTAL 30

TOTAL 40

TOTAL 43

Pizza pieces

Pizzas have to be cut into slices for different numbers of people. If each slice is exactly the same size, what angle should the pizza be cut with? The first one is done for you.

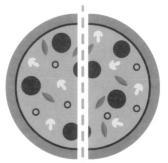

For 2 people: 180°

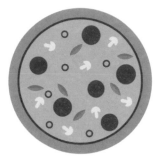

For 3 people: ___°

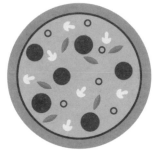

For 4 people: ___°

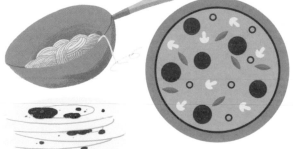

For 5 people: ___°

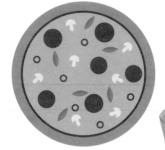

For 6 people: ___°

Alan Turing's Challenge

What angle would each slice be if you wanted to share the pizza between 8 people?

66

Working hours

Look at the firefighter's workday chart below.
How many hours was he at work from Monday to Friday?
Fill in the times in hours and minutes.

DAY	START	END	TIME
Monday	8.30am	5.40pm	
Tuesday	8.20am	6.17pm	
Wednesday	7.45am	4.35pm	
Thursday	9.05am	5.50pm	
Friday	8.52am	5.38pm	

Cake craft

Baking Belinda has 80 donuts to decorate but not enough toppings for every one.

She has enough …

… chocolate for 44.

… frosting for 28.

… sprinkles for 24.

… caramel for 16.

… cinnamon for 8.

What percentage of donuts get each covering?

Marine matches

Match the pairs of calculations that give the same answer.

4 x 12	20 x 4
70 ÷ 2	7 x 11
3 x 6	56 ÷ 2
32 + 32	6 x 8
7 x 5	8 x 10
7 x 6	64 – 13
90 – 13	9 x 2
4 x 7	17 x 3
54 ÷ 6	81 ÷ 9
8 x 8	29 + 13

Alan Turing's Challenge

Use the code on page 2 to discover a fun fact!

❄✦ ❄▲◎❄⌀◆◄ ▲❄✦ ◄★●☆☆✧☆ +◎◄ ◄❄▨◎ ◇❄◊◎

+✦◎❄ ☆▤◎◆☆✖☆▤○ ◎+✿△◎ ◄⌀❄▲☆◄⊙

69

Pixie tricks

This pixie has made most of the numbers in this grid disappear. Put the missing numbers from 1 to 9 into the empty squares to make the calculations correct. The numbers 1 to 9 can only appear once.

	+		-	1	=	11
x		x		+		
8	x		-		=	26
÷		-		x		
	+		x	9	=	45
=		=		=		
20		25		63		

Alan Turing's Challenge

Add up all the answers. What number do you get?

11 + 26 + 45 + 20 + 25 + 63

Shape sudoku

Copy the 9 different shapes into the empty squares, so that each row, each column and each 3x3 box of nine squares contains all 9 shapes.

Even odder

In this monstrous matrix fill each empty square with a number from 1 to 6.

No number may appear twice in any row or column. In sets of two squares separated by dotted lines, one square contains an odd number and the other an even number.

4		3			2
	5		1		4
				1	
5	6	2			
		4	2		
3			6	2	

Cool choices

On a hot, sunny day, everyone wants ice cream.

Ice creams cost $2.40, $2.50 with toppings, and $3 with a stick of chocolate.

How many of each kind could you buy with $25, leaving how much change?

How many of each kind could you buy with $12, leaving how much change?

Alan Turing's Challenge

What are the world's weirdest kinds of ice cream?

Chart toppers

This chart records how many albums have been sold each week.

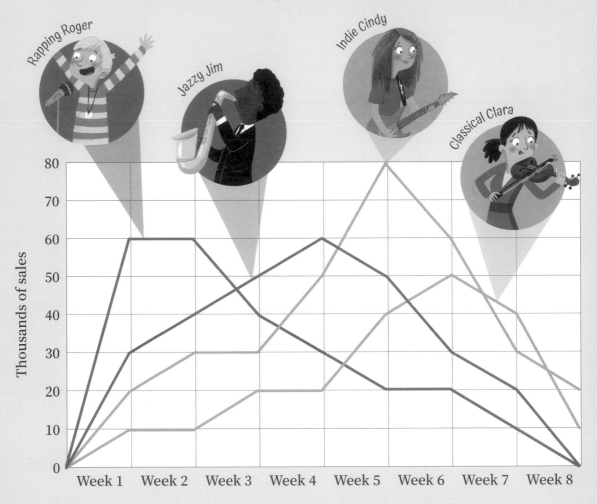

Over the 8 weeks, how many thousands of albums did each musician sell?

Who was the most popular? What were their average sales over the 8 weeks?

Pirate booty

Captain Patch is sharing out his treasure with his pirate crew. If the captain and his 3 crew members all get equal shares, what do they receive from the following?

24 gold coins

36 silver coins

12 bracelets

60 diamonds

48 rubies

84 emeralds

Alan Turing's Challenge

Captain Patch decides he will take half of everything, and divide the rest. How much will the rest of the crew get now?

Pond pals

How many of each type of duck visits the farm pond?

There are 130 ducks.

40% are male.

60% are female.

30% are ducklings.

10% are mostly white.

20% are mostly yellow.

70% are mostly brown.

Alan Turing's Challenge

If one fifth of the ducks build a nest, how many ducks is that? If each nest has six eggs, and all of the eggs hatch, how many cute baby ducklings will there be?

Primal quest

Goblin Gail is on a quest to find the Prime Dragon. Trace a path to the mighty monster, stepping only on prime numbers.

You can only move between touching tiles, and you cannot retrace your path.

Start

Finish

Who's the greatest?

Which numbers are bigger and stronger than the others?

Fill in the empty squares so that each row and column contains every number from 1 to 6. Follow the greater than (>) and less than (<) symbols as a guide to which number goes where.

Fast and fresh

At Freddy's Fast Food, the price for four items is shown at the end of each row and column. Can you work out how much each individual item costs?

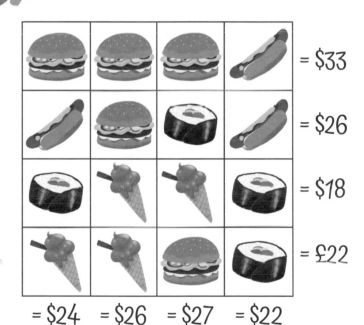

= $33

= $26

= $18

= £22

= $24 = $26 = $27 = $22

Alan Turing's Challenge

How many ice creams could you buy for $24?

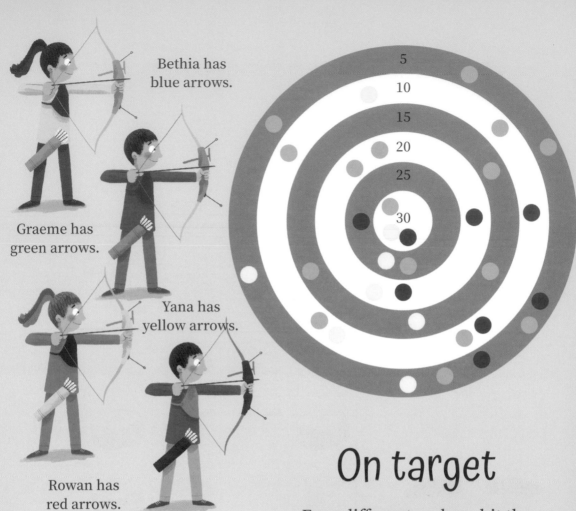

Bethia has
blue arrows.

Graeme has
green arrows.

Yana has
yellow arrows.

Rowan has
red arrows.

Bethia's score:	
Graeme's score:	
Yana's score:	
Rowan's score:	

On target

Four different archers hit the
target with eight arrows each,
scoring different amounts in
each band, from 5 in the outer
ring to 30 for the bullseye.

Add up the score for each archer's
markers on the target to work out
who won.

Going the distance

How far can each vehicle travel on a full tank of fuel?

Car 1 can carry 15 gallons of fuel and travel 30 miles per gallon.

Car 2 can carry 13 gallons of fuel and travel 32 miles per gallon.

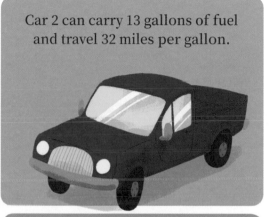

Car 3 can carry 16 gallons of fuel and travel 24 miles per gallon.

Car 4 can carry 12 gallons of fuel and travel 40 miles per gallon.

Alan Turing's Challenge
Use the code on page 2 to discover a fun fact!

△+⊛△♔❄○ ♣ +⤚ ❄●⤚◎◆❄▤+❄ +⤚ ◎△☆ ▤❄⤚⊛☆⤚◀◎

⤚❄◎+❄⤚❄▤ △+⊛△♔❄⤚ +⤚ ◎△☆ ♔❄⊛◆▤◖⊙ +◎

▤❄❄▱●◀ ❄◆❄●⤚◖◖ ◎△☆ ☆⤚◎+◆☆ ▲⊛●⤚◎◆○○

All square

This crossword has numbers, not words, for answers. Fill in the answers to the calculations one digit per square.

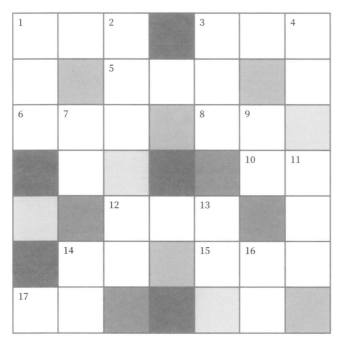

ACROSS

1. 461 x 2
3. 555 – 222
5. 20 x 20
6. Total of all the angles in a triangle
8. 8 x 8
10. 63 ÷ 3
12. 12 x 12
14. 6 x 6
15. 9 x 111
17. 8 x 9

DOWN

1. 1000 – 99
2. 480 ÷ 2
3. 400 – 94
4. 7 x 5
7. 9 x 9
9. 6 x 7
11. 91 + 48
12. 4 x 4
13. 7 x 7
14. 4 x 8
16. 46 + 46

Alan Turing's Challenge

Use the code on page 2 to discover a fun fact!

⊣❄⊣❋◇❋◎ ⬛ ❋◆☆ ◎+⊣○ ◆❋◇❋◎ ⬛ ◎△❋◎ ▲❋⊣ ◇☆

+⊣⌡☆▲◎☆⌡ +⊣◎❋ ○❋⬤◆ ◇❋⌡○⊙

Wild thing

Use the key at the bottom of the page to decode the pixelated picture and reveal a famously fearsome jungle creature.

The number 1 indicates white, the number 2 stands for orange, and so on.

8	8	8	8	3	3	3	3	3	3	3	3	3	8	8	8	8	8
8	1	1	1	2	8	8	8	8	8	8	8	2	1	1	1	8	8
8	7	7	2	2	2	5	5	8	5	5	2	2	2	7	7	8	8
2	2	2	5	8	8	8	8	8	8	8	8	5	2	2	2	2	2
3	2	5	5	1	1	8	5	5	8	5	5	8	1	1	5	5	2	3
1	8	2	8	5	4	1	8	1	6	1	8	1	4	5	8	2	8	1	1
1	8	2	1	4	8	4	6	6	6	6	6	4	8	4	1	2	8	1	1
1	8	5	2	1	4	8	6	2	2	2	6	8	4	1	2	5	8	1	1
1	8	5	8	6	8	2	2	2	2	2	2	2	8	6	8	5	8	1	1
1	8	1	8	8	1	2	2	2	2	2	2	2	1	8	8	1	8	1	1
3	1	1	1	1	8	1	2	2	2	2	2	1	8	1	1	1	1	3
3	1	8	8	8	1	8	6	2	2	2	6	8	1	8	8	8	1	3
3	1	1	8	5	1	1	6	2	2	2	6	1	1	5	8	1	1	3
3	3	1	8	8	1	2	1	6	6	6	1	2	1	8	8	1	3	3
3	3	1	8	5	5	1	1	6	8	6	1	1	5	5	8	1	3	3
3	3	1	1	8	8	8	1	1	8	1	1	8	8	8	1	1	3	3
3	3	3	7	8	1	1	7	8	8	8	7	1	1	8	7	3	3	3
3	3	3	3	7	1	1	1	1	1	1	1	1	1	7	3	3	3	3
3	3	3	3	3	7	1	1	1	1	1	1	1	7	3	3	3	3	3

1	2	3	4	5	6	7	8

Puzzle
SOLUTIONS!

No peeking here until you've given each puzzle your best shot! If you get stuck, try rereading the instructions carefully.

Solutions

Page 4

Group A is the five times table: 53 is the odd one out

Group B is the seven times table: 17 is the odd one out

Group C is the eleven times table: 111 is the odd one out

Group D is the three times table: 35 is the odd one out

Page 5

All the pairs should add up to 54. Pairs are:

5 & 49	16 & 38
7 & 47	17 & 37
8 & 46	19 & 35
9 & 45	21 & 33
11 & 43	22 & 32
12 & 42	23 & 31
13 & 41	25 & 29
15 & 39	26 & 28

Alan Turing's Challenge
Answer: 13

Page 6

Plate A
2 broccoli = 24¢, 4 carrots = 28¢, 9 beans = 45¢, 1 tomato = 9¢, 2 cabbages = 22¢.
Total = $1.28

Plate B
3 broccoli = 36¢, 5 carrots = 35¢, 7 beans = 35¢, 3 tomatoes = 27¢, 1 cabbage = 11¢.
Total = $1.44

Plate C
2 broccoli = 24¢, 3 carrots = 21¢, 7 beans = 35¢, 5 tomatoes = 45¢, 3 cabbages = 33¢.
Total = $1.58

Plate D
4 broccoli = 48¢, 6 carrots = 42¢, 5 beans = 25¢, 2 tomatoes = 18¢, 4 cabbages = 44¢.
Total = $1.77

Plate D is the most expensive.

Page 7

Juliet scooted at 10 m.p.h. for 10 mins, covering 1 2/3 miles, then 8 m.p.h. for 10 mins covering 1 1/3 miles = 3 miles in 20 mins so far. At 6 m.p.h. (or 6 miles in 60 minutes) it would take her 20 mins to go 2 miles. So, Juliet took 40 mins to cover 5 miles.

Dylan scooted at 12 m.p.h. for 15 minutes, covering 3 miles. At 6 m.p.h. it would take him 20 mins to go 2 miles. Dylan took 35 mins to cover 5 miles. He set off 5 minutes after Juliet, so they finished at the same time.

Billie cycled at 15 m.p.h. for 12 minutes, covering 3 miles. At 8 m.p.h. it would take her 15 mins to go 2 miles. Billie took 27 mins to cover 5 miles. She set off 10 minutes after Juliet. 27 + 10 = 37, so finished 3 minutes before both Juliet and Dylan.

Alan Turing's Challenge

Answer: Thirty percent of all trips in the Netherlands are made by bicycle.

Solutions

Page 8

$2^2 \div 2 + 10 \times 3 - 25 = 11$

$4^2 \div 2 + 10 \times 3 - 25 = 29$

$6^2 \div 2 + 10 \times 3 - 25 = 59$

$8^2 \div 2 + 10 \times 3 - 25 = 101$

$10^2 \div 2 + 10 \times 3 - 25 = 155$

Alan Turing's Challenge

Answer: the machine has not multiplied by 3.

Page 9

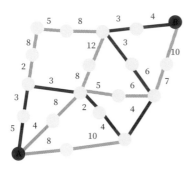

This route uses 37 tons of fuel.

Page 10

From lightest to heaviest, the pets are E, A, B, C, and D.

Page 11

There are 20 unicorns all together.

40% are blue. 30% are pink. 30% are neither pink nor blue.

20% have purple manes. 25% have yellow manes.

Alan Turing's Challenge

Answer: 28%

Page 12

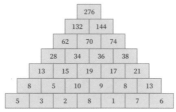

Alan Turing's Challenge

Answer: Servants of a dead Egyptian pharaoh were often sealed in his pyramid with him, dead or alive.

Page 13

1	9	3	4	8	7	5	6	2
6	7	2	3	5	9	4	1	8
5	8	4	2	6	1	3	9	7
2	6	5	8	1	3	7	4	9
7	3	9	6	2	4	8	5	1
8	4	1	9	7	5	2	3	6
3	5	6	7	9	2	1	8	4
4	2	8	1	3	6	9	7	5
9	1	7	5	4	8	6	2	3

Page 14

$75 each. 3 for the price of 2 = $50 per pair, $75 saving

¼ off $60 = $45 per pair, $15 saving

Was $84. Now half price! = $42 per pair, $42 saving

10% off $50 = $45 per pair, $5 saving

20% off $70 = $56 per pair, $14 saving

$1/_3$ off $60 = $40 per pair, $20 saving

30% off $80 = $56 per pair, $24 saving.

The cheapest pair is $1/_3$ off $60.

Alan Turing's Challenge

Answer: Was $84. Now half price!

Solutions

Page 15

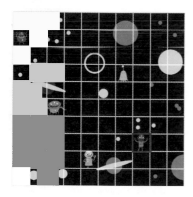

Page 17

Page 19

6

7

11

15

Page 16

Alan Turing's Challenge

Answer: Cosmonaut Gennady Padalka has spent 878 days in space over five missions.

Page 18

Brian won prizes worth 15, 40, 20, and 30. Total score – 105.

Jess won prizes worth 30, 30, 25, and 10. Total score = 95.

Martin won prizes worth 50, 15, 20, and 25. Total score = 110.

Cedric won prizes worth 30, 10, 40, and 25. Total score = 105

Martin won.

Alan Turing's Challenge

Answer: One 1st prize and four 3rd prize cups.

Page 20

There are 8 of the rarest jewels (pink) at $12 each. Total = $96.

There are 11 of the second-rarest jewels (yellow) at $9 each. Total = $99.

There are 25 red jewels at $13 for 5. Total = $65.

There are 24 green jewels at $9 for 3. Total = $72.

There are 32 of the most-common jewels (blue) at $6 for 2. Total = $96.

Total for all the jewels = $428.

Alan Turing's Challenge

Answer: Diamond is made from the element carbon, like the graphite in pencils.

Solutions

Page 21

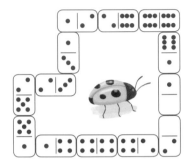

Page 22

$12 \times 5 + 4 = 64$

$8 \times 9 - 17 = 55$

$5 \times 10 \div 2 = 25$

$40 \div 8 \times 11 = 55$

$9 \times 6 \div 2 = 27$

$7 \times 5 + 13 = 48$

Alan Turing's Challenge

Answer: The earliest known use of the multiplication symbol in mathematics was in 1618.

Page 23

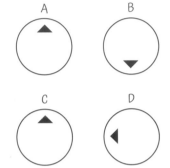

Page 24

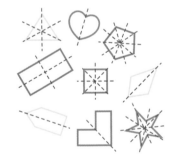

Page 25

3	5	8	12

Alan Turing's Challenge

Answer: The main difference is that cakes go hard when stale while cookies go soft.

Page 26

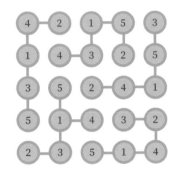

Page 27

A. 80

B. 64

C. 99

D. 8

Alan Turing's Challenge

Answer: It is not a multiple of 8. 99 is also the only odd number.

Page 28

	12	26		25	10
5	4	1	15 / 19	6	9
25	8	3	9	4	1
15 / 7	7	3	5		2 / 8
23	5	6	7	2	3
11	2	9	13	8	5

Solutions

Page 29

A after 3 hours reads 5.15, after 5 hours reads 7.25.

B after 3 hours reads 4.15, after 5 hours reads 5.45.

C after 3 hours reads 6.30, after 5 hours reads 9.30

D after 3 hours reads 3.00, after 5 hours reads 3.40.

Alan Turing's Challenge

Answer: The ancient Babylonians divided hours and minutes into sixty equal periods.

Page 30

374

Alan Turing's Challenge

Answer:
A. No
B. Yes, 374 divided by 11 is 34
C. No

Page 31

The temple is found in the square co-ordinate 7:3.

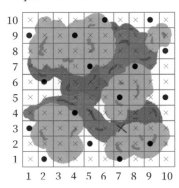

Page 32

$14 + 24 + 11 = 49 = 10 + 18 + 21.$

14	10
18	24
11	21

$17 + 31 + 9 = 57 = 6 + 23 + 28.$

17	6
23	31
9	28

$33 + 15 + 22 = 70 = 16 + 19 + 35.$

33	16
19	15
22	35

Alan Turing's Challenge

Answer: The indentation on a brick is called a frog!

Page 33

49

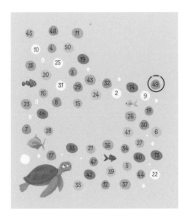

Page 34

Betty needs:

14 Beefburgers

4 Veggie burgers

15 Slices of cheese

2 Onions

4 Tomatoes

5 Gherkins

4 Servings of mustard

4 Servings of ketchup

Solutions

Page 35

6 x 6 + 3 = 39

2 x 6 x 25 = 300

26 – 4 – 18 = 4

50 + 29 + 3 = 82

9 x 4 x 2 = 72

100 ÷ 10 ÷ 10 = 1

Alan Turing's Challenge

Answer: 450

Page 36

5	7	6	3	2	8	9	6
2	8	1	8	4	7	1	7
6	5	8	2	9	3	8	5
1	9	3	7	5	6	2	4
3	5	8	4	9	5	8	7
8	4	9	6	7	4	5	2
3	7	5	4	5	9	8	6
9	3	8	3	8	5	1	7

Alan Turing's Challenge

Answer: This American inventor of musical instruments launched the first electric guitar in 1931.

Page 37

8-9am = 2 inches, 9-1pm = 4 x 4 inches = 16 inches, 1-3pm = 2 x 3 inches = 6 inches, 3-7pm = 4 x 2.5 inches = 10 inches, 7-9pm = 5 inches

TOTAL = 39 inches

Page 38

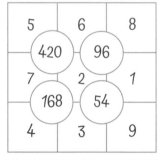

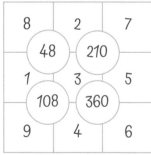

Alan Turing's Challenge

Answer: Cats cannot taste sweetness.

Page 39

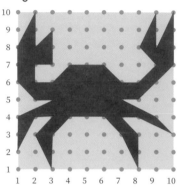

Page 40

$2^2 = 4$

$3^2 = 9$

$4^2 = 16$

$5^2 = 25$

$6^2 = 36$

$7^2 = 49$

$8^2 = 64$

$9^2 = 81$

$10^2 = 100$

$11^2 = 121$

$12^2 = 144$

$13^2 = 169$

$100^2 = 10,000$

Solutions

Page 41

70, 60, 51, 43, 36. (Each number goes down by one less than the number before, -10, -9, -8, etc).

3, 6, 10, 15, 21. (Each number goes up by one more than the number before, +3, +4, +5, etc).

2, 3, 6, 18, 108. (Each number is multiplied by the last).

1, 8, 27, 64, 125. (Cubic numbers: 1x1x1, 2x2x2, 3x3x3, 4x4x4, 5x5x5).

Alan Turing's Challenge

Answer: Elephants cannot jump.

Page 42

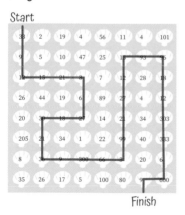

Page 43

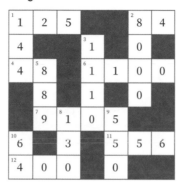

Alan Turing's Challenge

Answer: Jellyfish have no brains.

Page 44

Fred's patch is 20 square yards.

Paula's patch is 48 square yards.

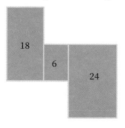

Alan Turing's Challenge

Answer: The first potatoes were farmed in Peru about 7,000 years ago.

Page 45

Group A: Remove 7 and 23.

Group B: Remove 16 and 19.

Group C: Remove 10 and 15.

Page 46

a. 40° c. 110° e. 20°

b. 35° d. 35°

Page 47

1. 350

2. Wednesday

3. They captured more criminals Thursday to Friday.

Alan Turing's Challenge

Answer: 60

Page 48

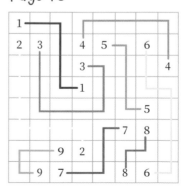

Solutions

Page 49

The burger, hot dog, and ice cream cost 2.25 all together.

Gary uses 3 x 50¢, 3 x 20¢, 1 x 10¢, 1 x 5¢.

Melanie uses 2 x 50¢, 5 x 20¢, 2 x 10¢, 1 x 5¢.

Alan Turing's Challenge

Answer: After buying his food, Gary has 85¢ left, so he does not have enough money to buy his friend a hot dog.

Page 50

5	1	2	2	3		7	9	3	9
	6			0			1		5
	6	2	2	4	8		2		2
	7			5	2	7	1	0	
5	1	2	1	4	7			0	
	5		8		7	3	6	5	
2			7		1			4	2
1	7	4	2	3	6		4		7
	9			5			5		
7	2	4		6	0	1	8	0	

Page 51

Car A takes 4 hours, 45 min.

Car B takes 3 hours 55 min.

Car C takes 4 hours 30 min.

Car B arrives first.

Alan Turing's Challenge

Answer: No. Car D takes 4 hours 5 minutes.

Page 52

The doctors got rid of 75% of the red rash germs, 40% of the blue goo germs, and 60% of the green meanies.

Alan Turing's Challenge

Answer: More than 40,000 droplets are sprayed into the air when you sneeze.

Page 53

41

Page 54

16

Page 55

This route adds up to 30.

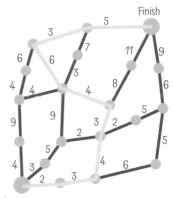

Alan Turing's Challenge

Answer: Yes, this route uses only odd numbers. It adds up to 32.

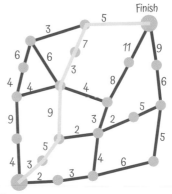

Solutions

Page 56

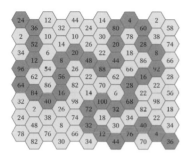

Page 57

Six squirrels would get 2 beech nuts, 4 acorns, and 6 hazelnuts.

Four squirrels would get 3 beech nuts, 6 acorns, and 9 hazelnuts.

Three squirrels would get 4 beech nuts, 8 acorns, and 12 hazelnuts.

Alan Turing's Challenge

Answer: Most squirrels cannot remember where they hide half of their nuts.

Page 58

Cindy covered (2 + 2 + 4½) x 2 miles = 17 miles.

Brian covered 6 + 3 + 1½ + 2 miles = 12½ miles.

Josie covered 4½ + 1 + 2 + 3 miles = 10½ miles.

Page 59

A. $^3/_4$ C. $^1/_4$ E. $^1/_5$

B. $^1/_2$ D. $^1/_3$

Alan Turing's Challenge

Answer:

A. 75%   C. 25%   E. 20%

B. 50%   D. 33.33%

Page 60

4 x 7 + 11 = 39

20 x 5 – 10 = 90

54 ÷ 6 x 5 = 45

36 ÷ 4 + 6 = 15

32 ÷ 4 + 26 = 34

Alan Turing's Challenge

Answer: 11 x 6 ÷ 3 = 22

Page 61

The ghost hunters captured a total of 44 ghosts.

Page 62

67	12	7	28	47	66	4	37	70	19	50	83
41	13	71	97	3	44	12	29	7	53	5	73
23	79	31	2	62	20	58	61	17	89	11	31
45	83	41	61	10	1	42	34	7	41	79	30
8	11	21	59	51	47	23	74	71	40	29	18
57	5	6	43	33	31	5	76	2	60	43	9
65	5	89	17	19	13	83	17	53	3	61	75
35	73	39	97	31	64	72	19	29	24	67	25
56	59	15	67	3	22	32	13	11	52	23	68
27	29	71	43	37	48	69	43	97	73	37	54
3	11	19	2	79	7	53	89	23	59	2	17
77	46	85	26	55	47	13	36	49	63	16	38

Solutions

Page 63

1. IX – II = VII
2. IV + VII = XI
3. VIII – V = III
4. XXII + IX = XXXI
5. XXX – IV = XXVI

Alan Turing's Challenge
Answer: XV + XXII = XXXVII

Page 64

Alan Turing's Challenge

Answer: In 2011 stuntman Freddy Nock set a new world record by tightrope walking between two Swiss peaks.

Page 65

11 + 15 = 26

7 + 23 = 30

19 + 21 = 40

3 + 40 = 43

Page 66

A circle is 360° so you have to divide this by the number of people.

For 2 people: 180°

For 3 people: 120°

For 4 people: 90°

For 5 people: 72°

For 6 people: 60°

Alan Turing's Challenge
Answer: For 8 people: 45°

Page 67

Day	Time
Monday	9 hours 10 minutes
Tuesday	9 hours 57 minutes
Wednesday	8 hours 50 minutes
Thursday	8 hours 45 minutes
Friday	8 hours 46 minutes

Page 68

55% of the donuts get a chocolate topping.

35% of the donuts get a topping of frosting.

30% of the donuts get sprinkles.

20% of the donuts get a caramel topping.

10% of the donuts get a cinnamon topping.

Page 69

4 x 12 and 6 x 8 = 48

3 x 6 and 9 x 2 = 18

7 x 11 and 90 – 13 = 77

7 x 5 and 70 ÷ 2 = 35

17 x 3 and 64 – 13 = 51

32 + 32 and 8 x 8 = 64

81 ÷ 9 and 54 ÷ 6 = 9

4 x 7 and = 56 ÷ 2 = 28

7 x 6 and = 29 + 13 = 42

20 x 4 and 8 x 10 = 80

Alan Turing's Challenge

Answer: An octopus can squeeze its soft body into extremely tight spaces.

Solutions

Page 70

5	+	7	-	1	=	11
x		x		+		
8	x	4	-	6	=	26
÷			-		x	
2	+	3	x	9	=	45
=		=		=		
20		25		63		

Alan Turing's Challenge

Answer: 190

Page 71

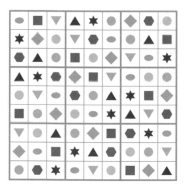

Page 72

4	1	3	5	6	2
2	5	6	1	3	4
6	2	5	4	1	3
5	6	2	3	4	1
1	3	4	2	5	6
3	4	1	6	2	5

Page 73

For $25 you could buy:
10 ice creams with $1 change.
10 ice creams with toppings
with no change.
8 ice creams with a stick of
chocolate with $1 change.

For $12 you could buy:
5 ice creams with no change.
4 ice creams with toppings
with $2 change.
4 ice creams with a stick of
chocolate with no change.

Alan Turing's Challenge

Answer: Garlic, curry, cheese
and pork are just some you
can try.

Page 74

Rapping Roger sold 60 + 60 +
40 + 30 + 20 + 20 + 10 + 0 =
240 thousand albums.
His average sales were
30 thousand albums.

Jazzy Jim sold 30 + 40 + 50 +
60 + 50 + 30 + 20 + 0 =
280 thousand albums.
His average sales were
35 thousand albums.

Indie Cindy sold 20 + 30 +
30 + 50 + 80 + 60 + 30 + 20 =
320 thousand albums.
Her average sales were
40 thousand albums.

Classical Clara sold 10 + 10 +
20 + 20 + 40 + 50 + 40 + 10 =
200 thousand albums.
Her average sales were
25 thousand albums.

Indie Cindy was the most
popular.

Page 75

Divided by 4, the captain and
crew each get ...

6 gold coins	15 diamonds
9 silver coins	12 rubies
3 bracelets	21 emeralds

Alan Turing's Challenge

Answer: If the captain takes
half, the rest of the crew get ...

4 gold coins	10 diamonds
6 silver coins	8 rubies
2 bracelets	14 emeralds

Solutions

Page 76

52 ducks are male.
78 are female.
39 are ducklings.
13 are mostly white.
26 are mostly yellow.
91 are mostly brown.

Alan Turing's Challenge

Answer: 26 ducks build nests.
There will be 156 ducklings.

Page 77

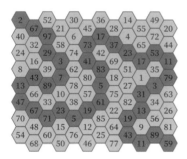

Page 78

3	6	2 <	5	4	1
4	2	3	1	6	5
6	3	1 <	4 <	5	2
1	4	5	2	3 <	6
2	5	4	6	1	3
5	1 <	6 >	3	2	4

Page 79

= $9   = $6   = $5   = £4

Alan Turing's Challenge

Answer: 6 ice creams

Page 80

Bethia scored 100.
Graeme scored 105.
Yana scored 120.
Rowan scored 125.
Rowan won.

Page 81

Car 1 can travel 15 x 30
= 450 miles.

Car 2 can travel 13 x 32
= 416 miles.

Car 3 can travel 16 x 24
= 384 miles.

Car 4 can travel 12 x 40
= 480 miles.

Alan Turing's Challenge

Answer: Highway 1 in Australia
is the longest national highway
in the world. It loops around
the entire country.

Page 82

¹9	2	²2		³3	3	⁴3
0		⁵4	0	0		5
⁶1	⁷8	0		⁸6	⁹4	
	1				¹⁰2	¹¹1
		¹²1	4	¹³4		3
	¹⁴3	6		¹⁵9	¹⁶9	9
¹⁷7	2				2	

Alan Turing's Challenge

Answer: Nanobots are tiny
robots that can be injected into
your body.

Page 83

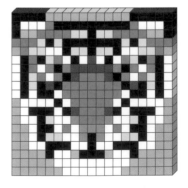

96